"Paddle",
Said the Swan

"Paddle," said the swan
in the pond by the sea.

"Fly," said the robin
to her young in the tree.

"Leap," said the frog as he jumped off the rock.

"Hop," said the rabbit.
"Crow," said the cock.

"Slither," said the snake
in the cool morning air.

"Twitter," said the sparrows.
"Trot," said the mare.

"Bark," said the dog to her puppies nearby.

"Honk," said the geese.

"Wash," said the cat.
"Squeak," said the mouse.

"Run," said the deer
to his speckled fawn and doe.

"Sniff," said the fox.

"Caw," said the crow.

"Coo," said the doves with a low, sweet sound.

"Ooh," said the baby, cuddly and round.

"Glow," said the fireflies,
"light up all the trees."

'Chirp," said the crickets
in the cool evening breeze.

"Hoot," said the owls
as they flew out of sight.

"Hush," said the mother, dimming the light.

"Da," said the baby,
snug in his crib.

Sleep," said
the mother ...

...and baby did.

Good night.